HEINEMANN MATHEMATICS 2

Name

MEASURE WORKBOOK

Revised

Length: non-standard units

1

Measure with clips.

The length is about ⑤ clips.

Measure the length of each.

about ☐ clips

about ☐ clips

about ☐ clips

about ☐ clips

about ☐ clips

Tick (✓) the longest. **Cross (✗) the shortest.**

Length: non-standard units

Measure with rods.

about 3 rods long

About how long is

    your table?   ___ rods

    your schoolbag? ___ rods

    the cupboard?   ___ rods

    the sink?   ___ rods

Investigation

Are all carrier bags the same width?

Bag	Width in rods
①	
②	
③	
④	

Which one is **widest**? _____

Length: non-standard units

3 Measure in feet.

Length of the cupboard	about ___ feet
Length of the table	about ___ feet
Width of the door	about ___ feet
	about ___ feet

Measure in spans.

Length of the cupboard	about ___ spans
Length of the table	about ___ spans
Width of the door	about ___ spans
	about ___ spans

Measure in paces.

About how long is

the classroom? ___ paces

the hall? ___ paces

the corridor? ___ paces

Walk 20 paces.

Who walks furthest?

_____

Measure using a long stick.

Length of the classroom	about ___ sticks
Width of the corridor	about ___ sticks
Height of the door	about ___ sticks

Weight: non-standard units

Balancing

The orange weighs ☐ cubes.

The pear weighs ☐ cubes.

Which weighs more, orange or pear? _____

Use cubes to weigh 📏 and 🖊.

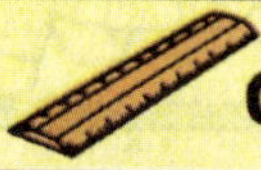

The ruler weighs ☐ cubes.

The pen weighs ☐ cubes.

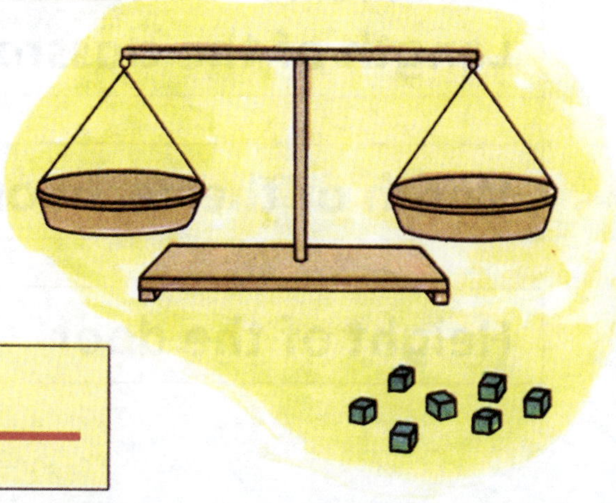

Which weighs less? _____

More balancing

Use pegs to weigh 🥕 🥔 🧅

The carrot 🥕 weighs ☐ pegs.

The potato 🥔 weighs ☐ pegs.

The onion 🧅 weighs ☐ pegs.

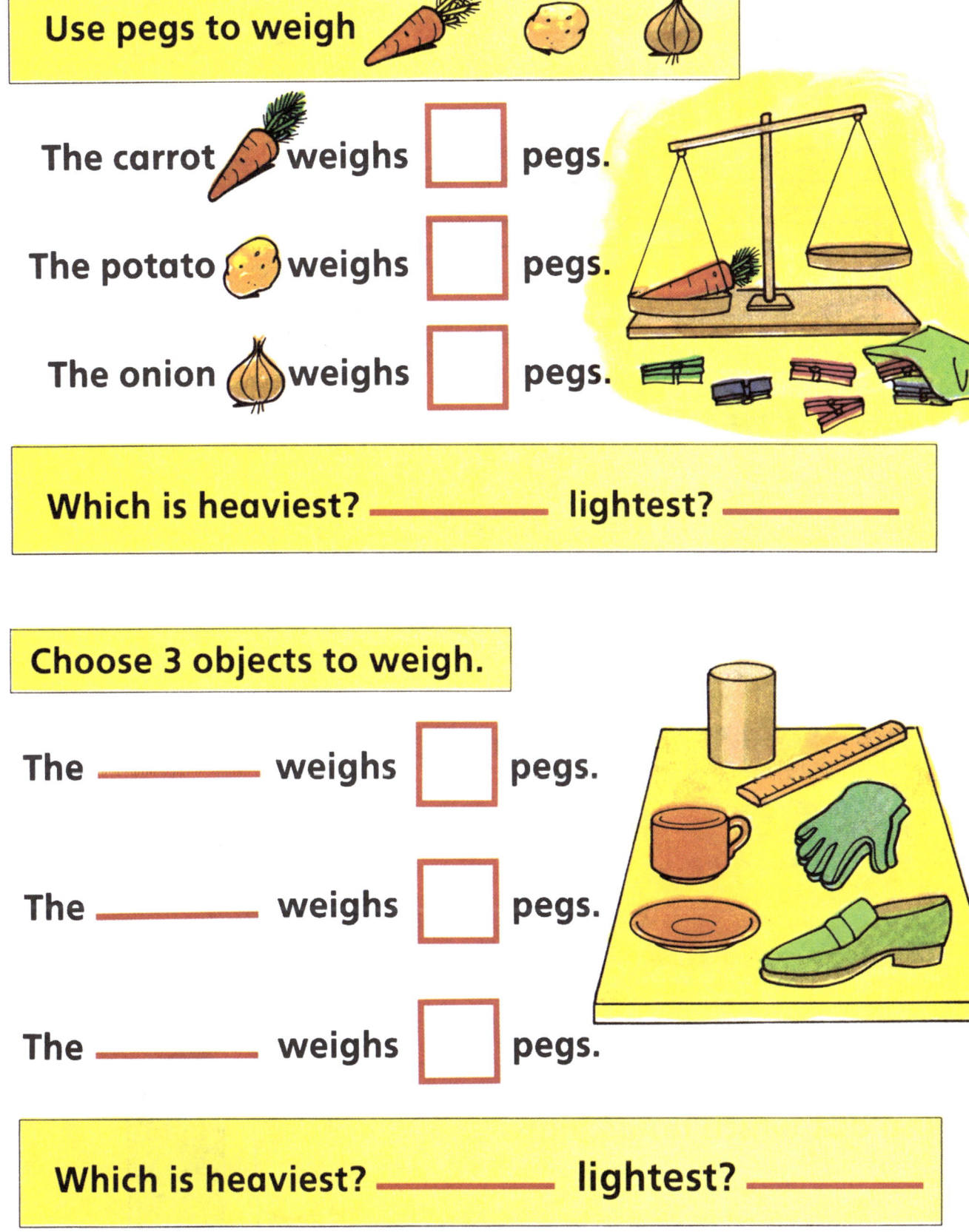

Which is heaviest? _____ lightest? _____

Choose 3 objects to weigh.

The _____ weighs ☐ pegs.

The _____ weighs ☐ pegs.

The _____ weighs ☐ pegs.

Which is heaviest? _____ lightest? _____

Weight: non-standard units

Cupfuls

Use a cup.

The 🪣 holds about ____ cupfuls.

The 🟩 holds about ____ cupfuls.

Tick (✓) which holds more.

The 🥣 holds about ____ cupfuls.

The 🍳 holds about ____ cupfuls.

Cross (✗) which holds less.

Extension

Find out which holds more.

Capacity: non-standard units

Ladles and spoons

Use a ladle.

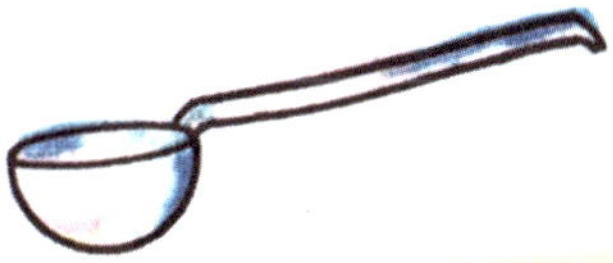

holds about ———

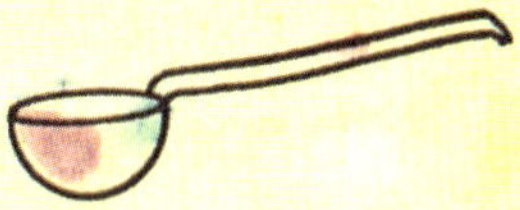

holds about ———

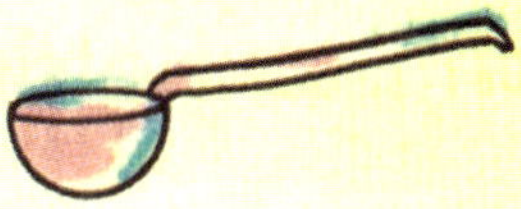

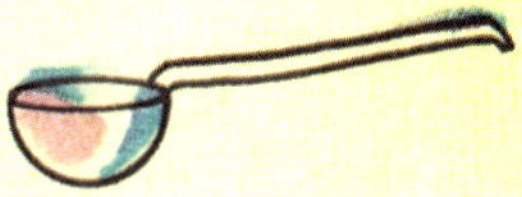

holds about ———

Tick (✓) which holds most.
Cross (✗) which holds least.

Extension

Use a spoon.

Find out which holds most.

Volume: non-standard units

Pack the boxes.

The 🔵 box holds _____ bricks.

The 🔴 box holds _____ bricks.

Which box holds more? _____

Use books.

Find out which box holds more.

_____ books   _____ books

Sea animals

For each pair, tick (✓) the one with the greater area.

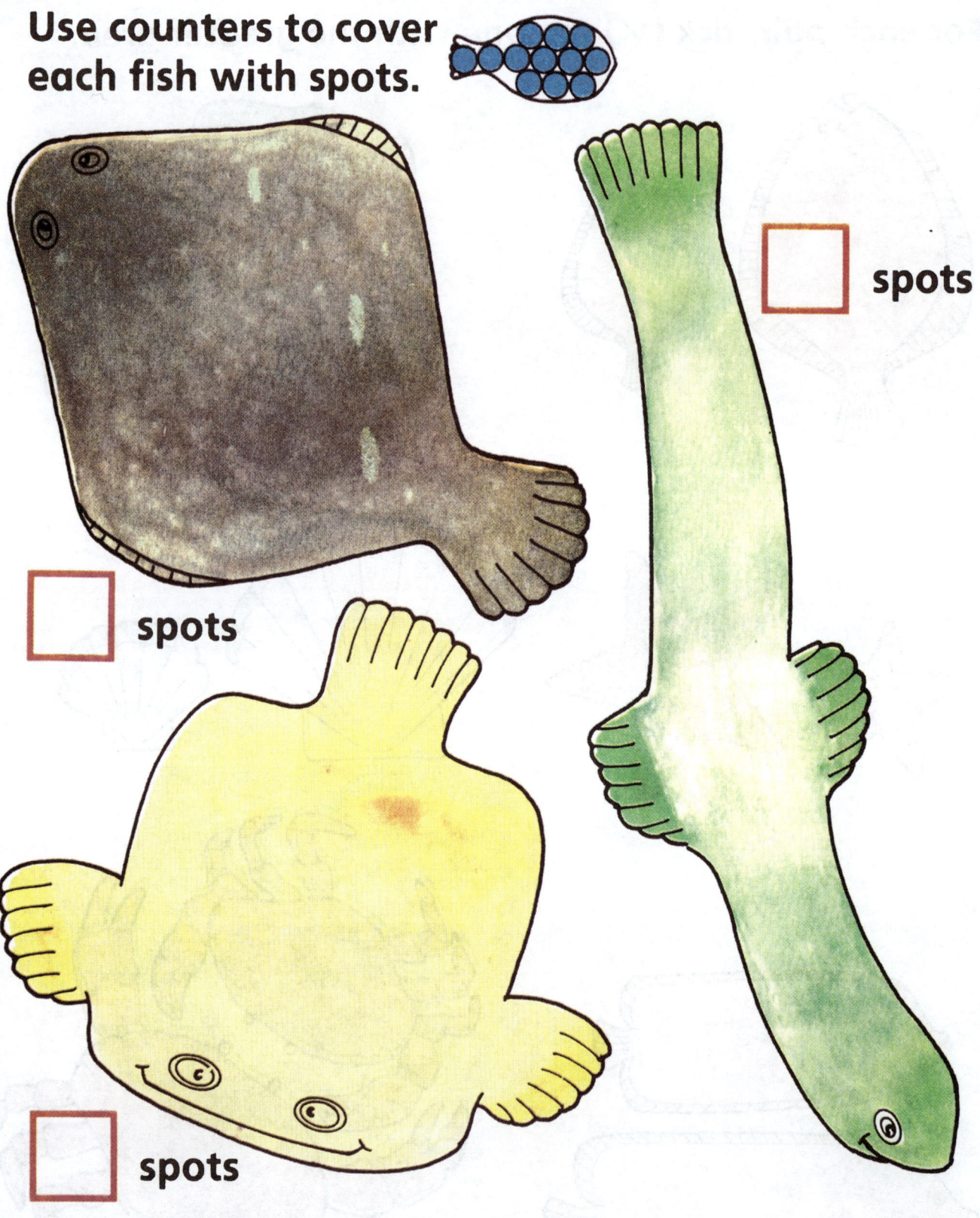

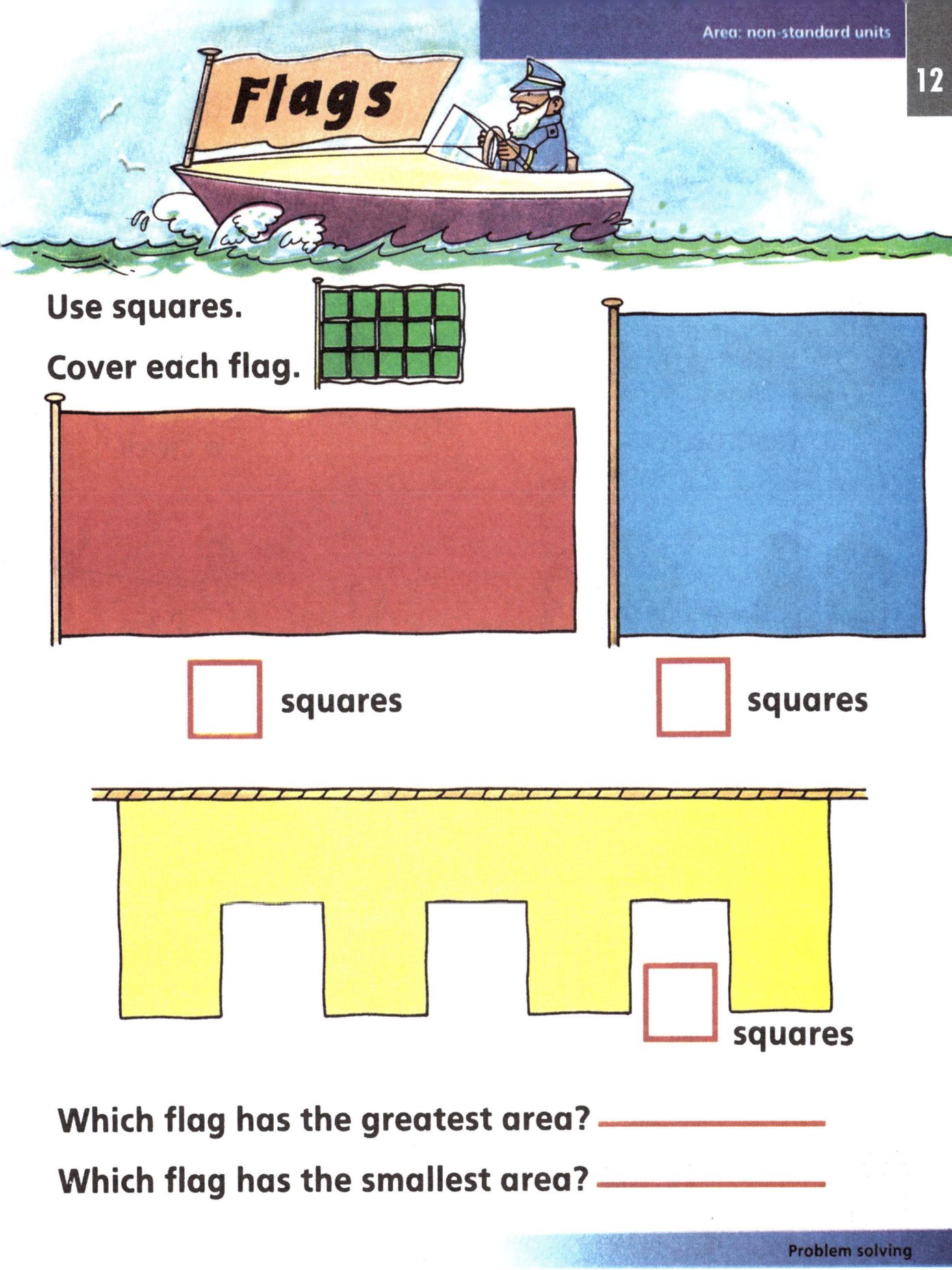

Safari park

half past

o'clock

half past ___

half past ___

Colour to match.

half past 12

half past 5

half past 6

half past 2

12 o'clock

Match

January

February

March

April

May

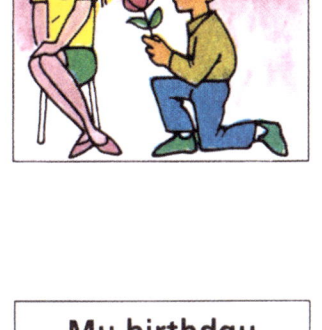

June

July

August

September

October

November

December

Pat's

Time: days of the week

Pat

Monday

Tuesday

Wednesday

Which day?

 _____    _____

 _____    _____

 _____    _____

Problem solving

Which day?

_____

Week

Thursday

Friday

Saturday

Sunday

Time: day before, day after

18

Write the missing days.

Monday   Tuesday   Wednesday

Thursday   _____   Saturday

Sunday   _____   Tuesday

Tuesday   _____   Thursday

Friday   _____   Sunday

Wednesday   _____   Friday

Today is _____.

Tomorrow will be _____.

Yesterday was _____.

Length — Extension/Investigation

The giant

Use your hands to measure your height.

My height is about ___ hands.

Talk to your teacher about your heights and about the giant's height.

Cut out the giant's hand.

Could he come into your classroom without bending down?

The giant's hand

Length

22

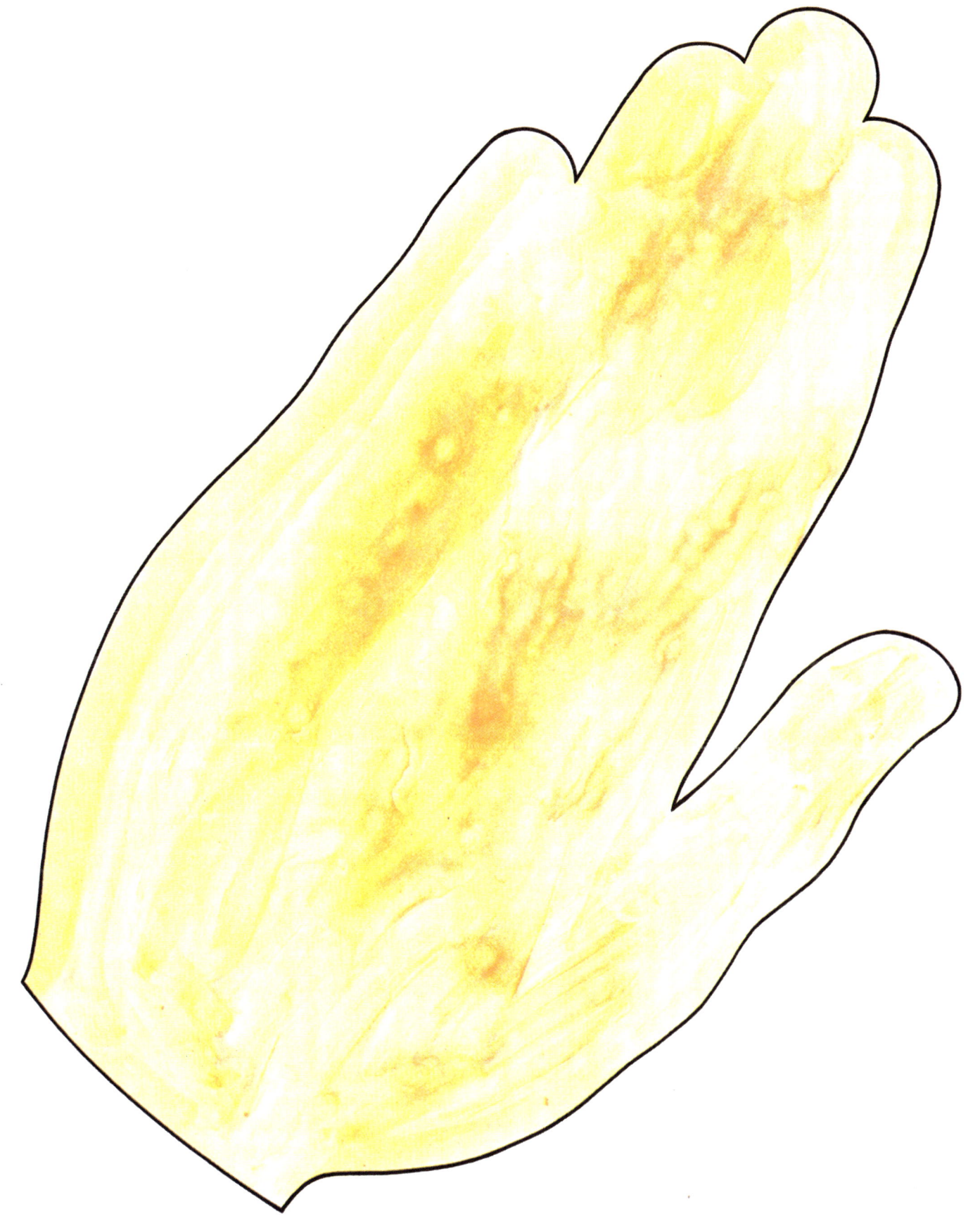

23

1	2	3	4	5	6	7	8	9	10	11	12	13	14	15	16	17	18	19	20	21	22	23

Heinemann is an imprint of Pearson Education Limited, a company incorporated in England and Wales, having its registered office at Edinburgh Gate, Harlow, Essex, CM20 2JE.
Registered company number: 872828
ISBN 978 0 435 03095 7 © Scottish Primary Mathematics Group 1981.
First published 1991. Revised edition 1995.   25   32
Typeset and Illustrated by Oxprint Design. Printed in Great Britain by Bell and Bain Ltd, Glasgow